THE DANGEROUS PLA

WHOOOO

Written and illustrated

by Nick Abadzis

For my brother, Alex.

This is THE PLANET ZARGON!

CHAPTER ONE

Meet Spiz and his older brother, Bex. They live on Zargon.

Bex, have you taken my book about spaceships?

Yes, I'm reading it.

But I want it. Give it back!

Ouch!

OK, OK. You can have it!

BOP!

Sometimes Spiz lets Bex tell him what to do.

It's boring anyway. Let's go and see what Uncle Gurt is up to.

4

No, this starcraft is too fast for boys to fly. You wouldn't be able to handle it.

Now it's time for you to go. I must get on with my work.

Uncle Gurt is wrong. I could fly that starcraft.

And I will, just you wait and see.

GROOBER & Cº

No, Bex, you heard what Uncle Gurt said. It's too fast for us to fly.

Hmmm.

But Bex wants to fly the starcraft. He wants to show Spiz he can fly at hyperspeed.

7

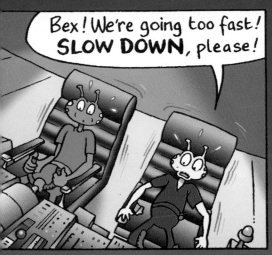

At last, the starcraft comes to a stop.

Phew!

But the small, blue world nearby isn't the planet Zargon!

Where are we?

I don't know.

We've got to get back home before Uncle Gurt sees that we've taken his starcraft!

?!

12

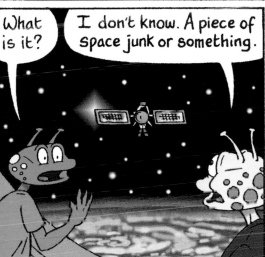

13

Tom Baxter is finishing his homework. He looks out of the window and sees a bright light racing across the night sky.

Hey, what's that?

It's going to land in the woods!

Tom climbs down the tree outside his bedroom window.

I've got to check this out before anyone else does.

After skidding through the trees, the starcraft comes to rest against the hillside. There is no movement from inside.

CHAPTER TWO

21

22

Soon, the area is crawling with more helicopters and jeeps. The starcraft is loaded onto a truck to be taken away to the Air Base.

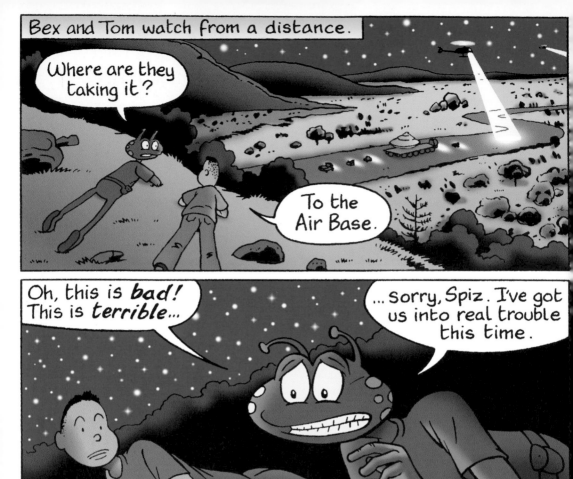

26

Inside, Spiz works to fix the starcraft...

Fix part B...

...to part M.

The starcraft is made from a super-metal from Zargon. They'll need something stronger than *that* to get in here.

Even so, I'd better hurry up.

Outside...

Muckley, get me the *top-secret* invention.

Yes, Sir!

Outside the Air Base...

We'll never get over that fence.

We won't need to.

KEEP OUT

I've got a penknife with me.

Cool! A penknife from outer space!

Yes. Watch...

...I can just cut a hole in the fence.

Come on. Let's find your starcraft!

31

CHAPTER THREE

The Giant Laser Beam is pointing at the starcraft...

We'll soon be ready to fire, Sir.

Excellent.

I've got to get back into the starcraft somehow.

I've got an idea.

You can just walk right over to it while they're all chasing me!

Thanks, Tom. Be careful.

34

37

Suddenly, there is a deep, rumbling noise. A huge shadow moves over the Air Base and blocks out the light of the stars and the moon.

Then the Air Base is bathed in a bright light.

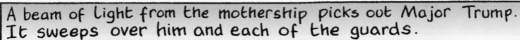

Ha-ha! I'm free!

It's a memory-changing beam. The Major and his men will fall asleep now.

They'll have no memory of what's happened here when they wake up.

We have to go now, Tom.

I want you to have my penknife as a gift for helping us.

Thanks, Bex

44

The starcraft is drawn up into the mothership. Bex and Spiz float up with it.

Then there is a flash of Light. The mothership has gone.

The Major and his men are sleeping.

Tom is the only person on Earth who Knows what has happened!

Back on the mothership, Uncle Gurt is very, very angry...

Bex, I have told you so many times not to take my things!

I'm sorry, Uncle Gurt.

As for you, Spiz...

No, Uncle Gurt. Spiz isn't to blame.

It's all my fault. I tricked him into getting onto the starcraft with me.

?

46

47